From Monks to Mud Men

by Mike Axworthy

First Published 2010 by Countyvise Limited
14 Appin Road, Birkenhead, Wirral CH41 9HH.

British Library Cataloguing in Publication Data.
A catalogue record for this book is available from the British Library.

ISBN 978 1 906823 42 9

FOREWORD

This work has taken me six months to complete, it is a result of many hours of research and interviews. I was not sure at the beginning what exactly I would end up with. Would it be a radio play? A book? A performance piece? In the final analysis the work is an amalgam of all three.

It is an attempt to chronicle 800 years of Garston history from the viewpoint of the people who lived it. It is not a history textbook as I have taken a little poetic licence with the characters in an attempt to tell a story. I decided the best way to bring the Garston story to life was to use ten characters, based on people who lived, worked or visited Garston and became part of the history, written and oral, of the Garston we know today.

In developing the characters and their stories I have used historical records, talked with Garstonians, young and old, listened to oral histories of families and finally, used my imagination and my own experience of living and working in Garston for over 50 years.

The main character the eternal fisherman of Garston shore is based on the men who fished the river with all its many moods, sometimes stormy, sometimes calm and also on generations of Garston men who have walked the shoreline over hundreds of years. I am one of them.

I hope you enjoy reading this book or alternately, watching a performance. Or why not give a performance yourself. After all it is our story. By the way 'Mud Men' or 'Mud Women' is a friendly term for people who lived on the banks of the Mersey, which as you know is a little muddy. Did you also know that one of the explanations given for the origin of Liverpool's name is from 'Liuerpul, which means 'Muddy Pool'.

I would like to thank the Garston Historical Society, who provided , Garston Community House staff who helped with typing, proofing and with general encouragement. Finally the good people of Garston who with their stories, humour, strength and love of Garston made this story possible.

This tale is dedicated to all Garstonians past and present and my family.

Mike Axworthy

The Eternal Fisherman

It's hard work – being a fisherman
I have fished this river for years.
I lived in a cottage on Garston shore on a great rock.
They tell me I drowned in the river, how could that be?
I am still here, or am I?
I will only die when the river runs dry.
Now I catch dreams and stories in my nets. I am going to tell
you the story of Garston from the monks to the men of mud.
I am part of their history and part of this river.
I have the river flowing in my blood. I am part of the tides –
the salt – the mud. I love the taste – the smell – the sight of
the river.
I love mud – the squelch and the smell of the mud.
I feel part of the crashing waves; feel part of the quiet waves
lapping on the shore.
I sit and watch and listen.

I have watched as Garston grew, watched the people
arriving.

I have watched as the monks - the fishermen - the salt men -
the docks - the railways - the industries - all came to Garston.

I have seen war and peace - prosperity and depressions -
slumps and now regeneration.

I will take you on a journey, a journey in time of a thousand
years.

I will cast my net into the silver waves and catch a dream, a
story of our first visitors...

'The Monks of Stanlawe'

That was a hard crossing rowing across the Mersey. I am a man of God, a monk. I have come to Garston to work and pray. Adam de Gerston has donated land and water below his mill to the monks of Stanlawe.

It is a common practice for rich men to give land to the monasteries. In this way they think they can gain favour and hope to gain a place in heaven.

I see there is already a chapel here in Garston called St. Wilfred's - that confused you - eventually in the mists of time this chapel will become the church of St. Michael, a long story - a long history.

Garston is a delightful place - God's own country. It stands on Garston River, a tributary of a mighty river, the Mersey, which has plenty of fish.

I love salmon on a platter with a jug of mead: a lovely dish fit for a king. No wonder I am fat: you never see a skinny monk.

We will build our mill on the Garston River, a fulling mill where we make cloth; we may also build a tannery for leather. We need cloth for our habits and leather for our sandals. I love the smell of leather – when it's finished – it stinks when we are making it.

Oh yes – we monks don't just pray you know. We sweat for the abbot. He doesn't work. He's the boss – nothing new there then.

Garston – that's a strange name, mind you so is Stanlawe, where our abbey is, across the Mersey.

Garston is not named after Adam de Garston you know, no, it is from the old English 'goers' or 'grass' and stan' meaning stone or rock. Put the two together, you have Gerston and looking at this beautiful place you have plenty of grass and massive outcrops of sandstone. The first mention of Garston was 1093, a long time ago.

Adam de Gerston also gave us land in Aigburth, which is part of the manor of Garston. We will build a grange there for our grain; yes we also farm as well.

We are Cistercian monks by the way also known as White Friars. Other monks who have been granted lands in Garston are the Benedictines of Upholland also known as Black Friars and they will build Garston Hall, which will stand on a sandstone outcrop overlooking the Garston River. It will have the Garston cross below it in the centre of Garston. The hall will stand for hundreds of years and the cross will be lost but one day it will be found – it now stands in St. Francis' churchyard – a miracle.

Garston Cross

Garston Hall

We are to move from 'Stanlawe' in the Wirral to Whalley in Lancashire (we have been granted more land and we will build an abbey there). Stanlawe is sinking below the waves so Whalley is the answer.

All was well for hundreds of years. We loved Garston and we made our contribution to your history. Maybe we got too rich and fat, because eventually in very turbulent times, Henry VIII sacked us all and shared the spoils with his rich barons, earls and lords. Our Abbot, John Paslow, was executed after the Pilgrimage of Grace uprising failed and all the monasteries were eventually dissolved.

Well that's our story, but life goes on, and it certainly did for Garston. We are away now; will never forget Garston. I was so happy; I hope heaven is like this.

The Eternal Fisherman

That was a good story or a sad one – depends on how you look at it.

Good riddance to them – ah maybe not, they were not a bad lot. Better the devil you know. Better the devil you know. I wonder who will rule the roost now. One thing, they can't have my river, it belongs to all us fisherman, mind you, I hear the Norris's of Speke Hall complaining about the fishermen here in Garston; – saying our stake nets and weir dams are taking all the salmon – I say there is enough for everyone.

Talking about Speke Hall, they themselves found themselves on the wrong side after all the troubles with the Church and monks. I'll cast my net, let's see what we catch – let's listen carefully to the tale of conspiracy, secrecy, hiding holes and most of all to a Poet-Storyteller, maybe we will learn more about the house in Speke and the Manor of Garston.

The Poet's Story

Shush Shush – I have to be quiet – The King's men will arrest me. I am a poet and storyteller and have been hiding in Speke Hall, I travel around Lancashire to all the old houses and manors who practise the ... (shush) the old faith.

Speke Hall - Manor of Garston

Speke Hall Woods

Shush – while I take you back to Elizabethan England to "Good Queen Bess" but our Bess was a good Queen, fair to all and as strong as any King, the daughter of Ann Boleyn who lost her head when she upset Henry VIII.

This Queen will not get married; she married England and defeated the Spanish Armada to become a heroine except with Mary Queen of Scots whose head she had chopped off. Bess must have got the idea from her dad, Henry of the six wives.

It was a time of conspiracy, secrecy, danger and execution – even for a poet like me. I keep my counsel – watch my back and most of all tell stories. Some true, some not. I am visiting Speke Hall as a guest of William Norris. He loves my poetry and plays; he has a lovely house and is very generous. I am hoping for a few florins before I leave his house and lands of Garston. I have visited a lot of manor houses in Lancashire, Knowsley Hall with the Queen's players and Rufford Hall in Ormskirk the home of the Heskeths. One day I hope to go to London to make my fortune.

Yesterday I visited Garston Hall. A lovely house built by Benedictine Monks on a rocky promontory overlooking the Mill Dam and Garston Cross. The monks have all been chased and their house and lands have gone to John Ireland, a very gracious host. After dinner I gave a performance, much appreciated by the gathered guests – Garston is a small village and everybody knows each other. When wine loosened their tongues it became clear they were unhappy. The church is closed, the endowment seized by the crown. I kept quiet – dangerous talk, walls have ears.

After my performance I left my hosts and walked back to Speke Hall. A beautiful place, Garston - the Dingle alongside the Mill and the Dale was a mass of flowers. The scent was heavenly and the bird song cheered my very soul.

A sad sight – the Chapel starting to crumble, my host William Norris hopes one day to rebuild the ancient chapel.

I could see the River Mersey in the distance where it is said the best fishing is to be had in the kingdom. A few cottages stand on the shore, these belonging to the fishermen – a very independent breed, separate from the villagers who are more gentle-folk.

I cross the fields, a straight walk between hedgerows across farm fields to a track called Banks Lane, until I reach Speke Hall.

As I walk I greet farmers working in the fields.

I enter the courtyard where two young yew trees have been planted, one called Adam the other Eve.

I am aware another guest is in residence – it is whispered, he hides in the walls behind the chimney. He is in danger if his profession is known. I will meet him soon.

That night I enter a small room, I see the cross, the candles, smell incense and then he appears (a Jesuit Priest). He looks pale after months in hiding but he comes to life when he begins to pray in the Mass – very dangerous. I leave the next day never to return, I go to London, I become famous as a playwright. Years later when people ask where did I go from Stratford when I went missing for two years? I don't tell them. "You won't tell will you"?

The Eternal Fisherman

I am pleased to say that the poet escaped with his life, others were not so lucky. Why oh why do these men of the church fall out so much? It seems so sad as the man they follow taught love and peace.

One thing I do know if the 'man of peace' came to Garston he would join me on the banks of the Mersey. He loved the sea and all his best friends were fishermen. I do not go to the church, I feel a bit smelly and rough. My church is the sea, sky and earth. I feel at home here and so did the 'man of peace'. Some of his best stories were about fishing. Once he helped his friends to catch lots of fish and nearly sank the boat. I heard he once calmed the sea or was it the fishermen he calmed? I can't remember now, and as for walking on water, well I don't know about that but I do know that you have got to have faith to be a fisherman. As for his request to his friends to be fishers of men, no thank you – I'd rather catch fish.

Men can be so evil – just listen to our next story. I'll cast my net and catch a dream or is it a nightmare – here she is a wronged woman – a victim of an evil man, she still pays the price now in stories maligning her. My friend forgives her as he says 'you should never hurt children, it would be better to put a millstone round your neck'.

Let's listen and learn.

Ginny Green Teeth

'Ginny Green Teeth' – the cheek of it - how did I get that name? That's what they call me, it's a sin. I was the victim and yet ever since I've had a bad name. People tell their children that I'm a child killer, a witch, a hag. They tell their children to stay away from ponds as I haunt them and will drag the children down to drown in the murky green depths.

How did this come about? You may ask – well I'll tell you. Listen as I recount the true story of my life and death and how my baby son died. How the man responsible told lies and spun tales of my so-called witchcraft so he would escape the gallows and in the process blacken my innocent name.

I was the happiest woman alive. I had a home, a husband and a beautiful baby son - I wanted no more.

8

We lived in a cottage on Banksfield; we had hens, a cow and two fields to grow all our needs. At the bottom of our fields ran the great river Mersey. To add to our diet my husband William Lightbody caught fish on the shore, getting help from the good fishermen of Garston. Life was hard but happy, too good to be true I thought and I was right. It was too good to be true. I knew it would not last.

Garston Cottage

One night William came home from the fields, he slumped into his chair looking frightened and said, 'I feel bad'. He was sweating and shaking, he knew he had caught the plague. Twenty people had died in Garston in the last few weeks; he would be next. William died two days later. I was heartbroken and frightened, was my baby or myself next? I buried William but I and my baby, John, survived.

I did not move for days, most of my neighbours tried to help but one had other ideas. Jack Stack said he wanted to help, he lived close by but my husband William knew him and avoided him if at all possible and so did I. William told me that Jack Stack had his eyes on our land and on me. He began to pester me, wanting to marry me; he said he'd give me a new life.

One night Jack Stack came knocking but I would not answer the door. He became louder, kicking the door and shouting 'let me in – or else'. I think he was drunk.

I was terrified, I held my baby tight as he cried. The door crashed open and he stood there. I screamed then ran for my life holding John close to me as I ran. I kept running towards the woods hoping that the trees would hide us, it was pitch black and I slipped on some mud down a bank, then splash! Oh the shock, the cold, oh my poor baby. I tried to scream and water filled my mouth. I struggled and felt for my baby's hand holding it tight. I felt myself sink down like a dream. I saw my William, my cottage and I went towards him slowly. We died painlessly.

Garston Mud

The local people came looking for us and found me and the baby clutching one another floating on top of a green covered pond, we had pond weed all over us. People thought that I had killed myself and the baby. I was overcome with grief they said and couldn't live without William.

Then the stories started. I wasn't cold in my grave before my character was blackened by a certain Jack Stack. Curious neighbours said to him, 'Didn't you visit

Ginnie after her husband died'? Jack, feeling that his guilt might be exposed decided to blacken my name.

He admitted that he had visited but told people that he had been scared off. He told them that I was a witch and had turned into a hag and when he was expressing concern about the baby I cursed him threatening to kill him and the baby if he came back.

So there it was, the story that I was a witch took hold, which they said was proved when they found us floating on top of the pond. 'Only witches float', they said. Over the years and then centuries, in local folklore I became the nasty Ginnie Green Teeth.

Children have since been taught to avoid ponds and lakes 'in case Ginnie Green Teeth gets you and drags you down'. What an injustice, I was caught in a web spun by Jack Stack, me, who loved my child and had been driven to my death by an evil man, had gone into history as a witch.

At least I have at last had the chance to tell my story and the truth has finally come out so in the future tell your children to avoid ponds and lakes because that bad man 'Mad' Jack Stack will get you.

The Eternal Fisherman

Don't time fly - days become years – years become centuries – before you know it Man will go to the Moon. I wonder if there are rivers and seas there to fish in. If not, I'm staying here in Garston on the river.

The tales move on - it is now the 1800s – Garston is growing and the river is changing. More ships sail the seas, some built here in Garston. Fishermen are under pressure.

People are claiming to own the shore and have fishing rights to the river.

They are also sharing the land out – enclosure they call it – a crime I call it. People are losing their common lands and we are losing our cottages. I yearn for past times but time stops for no man. I hope for heaven – when I fulfil my destiny – what that is I don't know yet. I am getting tired of being the Dream Catcher of Garston. Give me my net and let's see what I catch. Here it is – a ship – a pirate – a tale of the high seas and high office – of riches and ill-gotten gains – a true story. Shush let's listen – here's the pirate – listen to his story – you will be amazed.

The Pirate – Privateer

I am no pirate- do I look like Blackbeard? I had no Skull and Crossbones.

I am a respectable man – A Privateer – in other words a respectable (Pirate).

I learned a trade – I started as a carpenter, yes, and a good solid trade especially in the days of wooden ships. I built ships on the shores of Garston; the biggest was the *Kent*, the largest ship in Lancashire at the time.

Then I heard whispers in Liverpool of a lucrative trade on the Seven Seas. It was known as privateering and for this I would need a ship and a licence. Yes, a licence – better known as Letter of Marque – not Mark – but M-A-R-Q-U-E. In other words this gives authorisation from the government to plunder any ships from any country across any frontier – if we had enmity toward them.

I received my warrant, my commission to act as a Privateer; all I needed now was a ship.

I went back to Garston and built the mighty *Mentor*. It had 28 cannons and a crew of 100 men.

I now needed a Captain – what better man than my brother-in-law, John Dawson – keep it in the family eh!

So off they set – my ship – my crew and Captain Dawson.

For a year or two trade was bad, we never boarded or captured any ship. We were especially after Spanish or French ships as they were known to carry rich cargoes and the British Government, short of declaring war on them, wanted to get even with them for past misdeeds.

Then one day the answer to all our prayers, we came upon a French ship, the *Carnatic*, a lightly armed ship smaller than us. Just perfect! We shot at it, and then boarded immediately – it didn't take long for the French to surrender.

Garston Docks

Then Eureka! Treasure beyond our wildest dreams, diamonds and gold – in one box we found diamonds worth £35,000 – in total the booty was worth over half a million pounds – nowadays about 25 million – I was made for life.

What would I do with such an amount of money? – I know – I will buy Garston, yes BUY Garston – the man who started as a carpenter would own Garston – I had heard Thomas Beauclerk – a posh name – had sold Garston Manor to the City of Liverpool but he had fallen on bad times. He had connections to the Norris family of Speke Hall – in fact he was said to be the great grandson of Charles II and Nell Gywnn.

I am not surprised at that – Charles II had children all around his realm to various mistresses. Not a bad job – King eh!

Anyway, back to me. I put an offer to Liverpool they could not refuse! And they sold Garston to me. They made a mistake there – it would be another 100 years before Garston finally became part of Liverpool again.

Not long after I became "Lord Mayor of Liverpool" – me a Carpenter, a Pirate I mean a Privateer, a Rich Man – maybe that had something to do with it – my money? We won't say anything about that eh!

I also built a big house in Mossley Hill looking down on the River and Garston shore. I called it Carnatic Hall, what else? But would you believe it – no sooner had I made my money I went and died – nothing my money could about that – what a pity.

Still it was good while it lasted. Remember – I was a privateer not a pirate.

North Dock, Garston

The Eternal Fisherman

How about that story? Maybe I'm in the wrong trade! Catching fish doesn't pay much, not as much as Piracy, sorry

Privateering! No way, I love my fishing – I love my river. Greed is a devil, money is an evil. Anyway you can't eat money – give me fish any day.

We will probably lose our fishing berths soon and our cottages. The Salt Works are coming, they need docks, land and sea-water and they want us on our way.

We will move our boats further up the river; our staked garths and fishing weirs are still safe thank goodness.

Still we can't be selfish; the river belongs to us all – I just hope you look after it for our children.

Just imagine how did salt get into the sea, and just enough for the fish and to stop the sea from freezing? Another miracle, all creation is a miracle. I am not clever enough to understand it all, I just thank God and treasure the earth, the moon, the stars, everything.

Listen, I can hear the salt works – it's started – it smokes and it's smelly and the men work hard to earn their money. They have to buy fish and bread; we catch fish and make our own bread.

The Salt Boiler

It's hard work being a salt boiler; at the end of day, I am so tired and thirsty I visit the Blackburne Arms for a quick pint or two or two – I'm in for a telling off from the wife.

What's a salt boiler you ask? I can see your confused looks – well I boil salt – obvious isn't it, but wait a minute – I'll explain. Garston had a massive salt works in the 1800s, it opened in 1798 after it moved from Liverpool – they couldn't stand the stink – and John Blackburne the owner of the Salt Works and the Landlord of the Blackburne Arms, thought Garston would not mind – nothing's changed there then!

ROCK SALT MINES.
WINCHAM & MARSTON.
NORTHWICH - CHESHIRE.

Garston Salt Works.

WAREHOUSE.
NOVA SCOTIA.
LIVERPOOL.

Still Garston has been a great place for my family – I have a job – we have a cottage and best of all food, when we left Ireland – you might have guessed by the accent – we were starving. The crops had failed and people left Ireland in droves, some to America some to England, - anywhere but Ireland. So sad, the Great Famine – a million people have died. Liverpool was first port of call for many and many stayed – some even came to Garston and I am pleased I came here.

I forgot to tell you, John Blackburne IV owned the Manor of Garston so had no trouble finding a place for the Salt Works – it's right on Garston Beach next to the Old Dock, opposite Garston Rocks and the Mud Banks. I won't give you a chemistry lesson, but I'll tell you a little about Garston Salt. First of all it comes from Northwich as Rock Salt, in boats called Mersey Flats. It

Schooner

16

unloads at Garston then goes into salt ponds to dissolve; this happens when the tide comes in and helps dissolve the rock salt. When it turns to brine it goes into large cast iron tanks, then the brine is boiled, that's where I come in. I load the furnaces with coal – it was hot and hard work (good for the muscles). Eventually after boiling we ended up with salt crystals in the pan. (That's enough of the lesson). The salt went all over the country. Garston is still a small place with about 2,500 people living here. We live in a cottage – sometimes called The Piggeries – a bit unfair. The bosses live in Blackburne House – there you are Blackburne House again. My wife is a domestic servant for Mr Blackburne – I'd better watch what I say.

It was dangerous work, men died, drowning in the dock or falling under trains. Even our children died young from measles or whooping cough or even falling into the dock. Hard times indeed but I'm not complaining - it could be worse.

There are a few Irish here like me escaping starvation, but most of my mates are local Garston men, a good breed. There are also men and women from all over Lancashire. So next time you have salt on your dinner think of us men, known as Garston Salt Men – Salt of the Earth.

The Eternal Fisherman

Time is passing so quickly now. The river keeps the same time – what do they say – time and tide wait for no man. But everything is changing so fast it frightens me. Our Garston River front and town is expanding so quickly, nothing changed for hundreds of years now changes happen in days. What was our life blood, the river and the fishing – is now being developed so fast. We are getting pushed out and with the docks expanding come the railways, come the industry, come the houses and the people. In 1841 two thousand people lived here and by 1881 the number had rose to eighteen thousand.

Oh I forgot Garston has a new parish church, St Michael's, the third one on the site and I can still remember

the first one and the Monks. Because we have so many people coming from Ireland, Wales, Scotland and England, churches and missions of different denominations are opening all over Garston. Ah - it was so much simpler in the old days. I cry for my river, it

Ship and tug at Garston Docks

is starting to get polluted, the fish will die and the fishermen with it (they call this progress?)

In the last fifty years from 1841 we have seen a growth of industrialisation, turning Garston from a small rural backwater into a major industrial power – is this good? As my friend William Blake wrote in his poem "Jerusalem" we are turning from a green and pleasant land to a place of smoking chimneys and dark satanic mills.

It's now 1900, the beginning of the 20th century and here are the big industries in Garston.

1863	Brick Manufacturers Tushingham – (Rita Tushingham, the Actor, it's her family) – well we need them to build the houses for all the workers.
1864	Garston Iron and Steel Company
1865	John Bibby & Sons Copper Works
1868	Rawlinson Saw Milling and Builders
1869	Blackwells Metallurgical Works
1880	Crown Copper Works

1880   *Francis Morton Iron Works*
1892   *The Gas Works*
1899   *The Garston Tannery*

I'll cast my net for a story, I am curious as to what I will catch, ah! I can see and hear our friend. At last, a woman to tell her story. She has travelled from Todmorden to Garston to work in the Bobbin Works.

And now, after hundreds of years of independence, Garston has joined Liverpool – incorporation they call it, I call it being swallowed up!

The Bobbin Worker 1911

I started my job at the bobbin works in 1902, the beginning of a new century; I was 14 years of age. I needed to get a job and my father got me a start in the bobbin works. Father has worked for Wilson Brothers for 30 years; he came to Garston with the company in 1892.

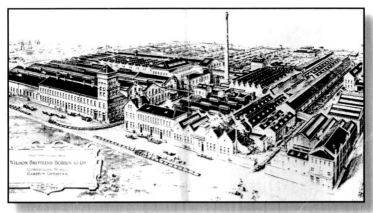

Dad and the company came from Todmordern in Lancashire and this is where the bobbin and shuttle works began, supplying to the growing cotton industry in Lancashire and Yorkshire - it was industry that made England rich. Dad is a sawyer in the saw mill, one of the men who started a social club in Window Lane called the Sawyers Club which later became the Woodcutter's Social Club.

Bobbin Works

So it was no surprise that when I left Garston C.E. School I would end up in a factory with over a thousand employees, the biggest bobbin works in the world.

I live in York Street with Mum and Dad, a few years later to be shared with my husband William and two children. The house is a bit small, it only has 4 rooms, two up, two down, no bathroom or indoor lavatory and no hot water. William wants us to get our own house, he might be able to if he kept out of the pubs, by the way William works in the Brickfields. So we all fall out of bed to go to work. Mum keeps house and looks after the children. I think she longs for her own little cottage in Todmordern. She never wanted to come to Garston and its streets and factories – the smoke and the smells and the trouble.

Oh yes, the trouble. I forgot to tell you, Dad is on strike he has been so for ten weeks, all the sawyers have been and a lot of the women as well.

My Dad's not talking to me, I am not on strike and he calls me names – horrible names but I need the money for my kids and a house of my own. Mum is a peacemaker or tries to be, she goes to St. Michael's a new church the third on this site and prays for us all.

The strikers had a march last week up Window Lane behind the Sawyers own band "The Orange and the Green" a drum and fife band. It ended in a riot and what Dad called Police Brutality, women and children were caught up in it, the strikers attacked the tram bringing in what they called Scabs, from town.

Dad said they had no right coming into Garston taking our jobs. I said "go back to work then" and he nearly hit me, luckily Mum was there to bring peace.

I hope it is settled soon, the whole world is going mad, my Dad says "pay us a fair wage and we will be back".

In the meantime I'd better go to the shops for some more tea, the kids need feeding as well as Dad and William – they will probably come home after a couple of pints demanding their tea. That's why I'm not on strike; we have to have money for food and rent. Mr Wilson the Big Boss made it clear to the strikers –"you can either come back to work or end up in the workhouse" – and he is right - there's no money from anywhere else, no social security only charity or the workhouse.

No, I can't afford to have principles, we have to eat. In my heart I support the strikers but I have to swallow my pride and take the abuse and anyway who pays for their beer and our bread?

The Eternal Fisherman

I could cry.

It's 1940 and my river is starting to die.

The world is at war with Germany, a country that gave us Beethoven is now ruled by a despot, Hitler, "how sad".

I thought they would have learned only 20 years ago when we had the First World War and millions died many from Garston.

Will they ever learn? It's different now; they come here and drop bombs on us.

When I was a lad the only things that could fly were the birds – now in the blink of an eye man can fly – and what does he do? He drops bombs from his flying machines. I don't think the Wright Brothers had that in mind when they first flew.

I suppose that's progress, better ways of killing you.

Never mind - one thing about Garston is its people, there are angels here. A great spirit, the people in the community help and support each other – they are strong – they work hard and they certainly know how to enjoy themselves.

I have watched as people came. They have built a community that's strong. There are churches everywhere – there's a hospital and shops for everything – plenty of pubs and clubs and schools for all.

Yet let's look now.

There's danger in the air.

Families are being split up.

Children separated from mothers and fathers. Son's separated from families. Wives saying good-bye to husbands.

Let's take a look.

I will cast my nets, catch a dream, and hear a story – one young girl's story, a story of bravery – of hope – of community under fire and about the spirit that shone brightly in the dark.

The War Child

I was born in 1928, ten years after the end of the First World War in which millions died. I was told it was the war to end all wars and must never be allowed to happen again. Now here we are in 1939 and war is declared again.

My Mum told me first and it frightened me but at first not much changed. I still went to Banks Road School, I still played with my friends in the street and my Dad still went to work in Garston Tannery. My Mum still went to the Wash House. We lived in Ultonia Street under the bridge in Garston. I was born in this house and my Mum and Dad moved in when it was first built. They previously lived with Granny and Granddad Jones. My Great Ninny Jones lived with them as well. She was old and sat in a chair in her shawl and bonnet knitting

Maypole Dancing in Garston, 1928

all day. She didn't speak much and when she did it was in Welsh, she had come to Garston with her husband Hugh who had come to Garston to work in Bibby's Copper Works. Great Ninny Jones could speak a bit of English but chose not to. I don't think she ever wanted to come to England as she was proud of being Welsh and loved Anglesey where she once lived. I loved our new house; it was small, two up – two down like hundreds of houses around us, a lavatory down the yard and no bathroom. But we were happy and we were clean, we had a tin bath and boiled water to fill the bath in front of the fire grate. On special days I went to Garston Baths for a slipper bath.

Then it all changed – in school they talked of evacuation, what was that I asked? Going to a safe place – leaving home I was told. This filled me with dread – I loved my Mum and Dad, I could not leave – I would stay; and stay I did, for a while at least. I watched as things changed, men in the street went to war, brothers, dads and uncles. Men were seen proudly wearing their uniforms – boys turned into men.

Mum put thick curtains up to black out the house. We turned gas lamps off and used candles, it was cosy sitting with Mum in candlelight, cuddled up in front of the black range with its kettle boiling and fire burning.

Rationing was brought in, my Mum had a ration book – things were a bit short but Dad had an allotment and grew our own vegetables. He even caught the odd rabbit down the shore that my Mum made into rabbit pie. We even had fish sometimes, caught in the Mersey by a family friend who lived behind us in Etruria Street.

I asked Dad if the Germans would attack us. "Yes" he said, "We have docks, railways, lots of industry, an airport and lots of streets with plenty of people. Garston is now a very big area - but don't worry," he said, "We will batter them."

Air raid shelters were built in the schoolyards, in people's gardens or in back yards, underground, everywhere and they were fun at first to play in.

My Mum got a job at Rootes, making war armaments like tanks and guns; she said she was helping the war effort.

My Dad was too old to fight he said, but was doing his bit in the Tannery making leather soles. "Men would need leather for boots" he said to march to war.

Garston was spared the worst of the Blitz, the docks at the north end got flattened, as did the Town Centre and many people died in those areas.

Then one night on the 28th November 1940 Garston got one almighty shock. A land mine landed in one of the gas tanks and

Garston Parish Church and gas tank

the whole of Garston "under the bridge" was evacuated. If the land mine exploded Garston was in great danger. Then a hero came to our rescue. A Captain Newgass, a Bomb Disposal Officer climbed into the giant gas tank to defuse the bomb. He was not the only hero, Garston men who worked at the gasworks helped in the operation.

We were evacuated to my Aunty Lil's up in the village as all this went on. After a few pints Dad said "I'm going home". He grabbed my hand and I followed. By the bridge there was a rope across the road and that meant no-one was allowed to pass. My Dad, headstrong or maybe a bit drunk, said "I'm passing, I'm going home". Then a policeman said "You're not going anywhere" and blocked him. I got a bit scared then eventually Dad grabbed me and angrily went back to Aunty Lil's where my Mum gave him an even bigger telling off, calling him "a stupid git" and told him to go to bed. So I will always remember the gas tank bomb.

After this bomb and another hit the school Mum said "I'm sorry, you are leaving this town for your own safety".

I cried but as many of my friends had already gone to places like Southport, Wales and Lancaster, I accepted with reluctance. I packed my cardboard suitcase sadly carried my gas mask on my shoulder. I cried buckets as I left. My Dad stayed away, he couldn't say good-bye, and it broke his heart.

It was arranged for me to go to Llangollen. We went on a train with other children and at the station we were met by some ladies, who took us to the Village Hall. We were all lined up and then people picked us out and took us home. A Dr. Alexander and his wife took me to their house overlooking the Llangollen River. It was a beautiful house on a beautiful river in a lovely town, and Dr Alexander and his wife were caring people just like a real Mum and Dad.

As nice as it was at Llangollen it was not home. I missed our house, I missed our street and most of all I missed Mum and Dad. I worried that they might be killed – I cried myself to sleep most nights. Some of my friends were homesick they went home after a few months. Their hosts in some cases were not as caring as our lovely Dr. Alexander.

We knew little of Garston and what was happening back home, just snippets of information given to us by Miss Steward our teacher. One day she told me my Father was coming next day and I would need to pack. I had been in Llangollen for nearly two years, and would miss it and our adopted parents, but I realised there is no place like home.

Father arrived to take me home and we never stopped talking all the way home on the train. He told me I had developed a Welsh accent, I sounded like my Granny Jones.

On arriving in Garston not much had changed, the war was still on but it was quiet at the moment. Dad said we were winning the war. I was sad though when I saw the bomb damage in Saunby Street, a big gap in the street where was once there had been houses, showed it had not been all quiet. Ten people killed and lots injured when the bomb dropped on the houses – it must have been awful.

I was now fourteen, had left school and got a job in Mapletons up in the village. I packed nuts. Dad still worked at the Tannery; Mum worked at Roote's and played the piano in the Canterbury Pub.

Then we heard rumours the war was nearly over, we were winning. It was 1945, I was now 16 and felt grown up, My Dad was still a little strict, I couldn't stay out late and if I went to the local dance like the Winter Gardens in Heald Street, he would meet me, making sure I got home safely and without any boys.

Then a moment I will never forget, the announcement by our great leader Winston Churchill, that the war was over. We were victorious, people poured out into the street cheering and clapping and hugging each other.

Then on V.E. Day we had a big party in our street.

Bunting was put up, flags decorated, windows and lamp posts were painted, tables put in the street, food and drink overflowed despite the rationing and to top it all, our piano came outside for my Mum to play. Then all the street, neighbours and friends had a great

York Way street party

party, singing and dancing into the small hours. I toured the other street parties with friends – Garston knew how to celebrate.

Mind you, some people were sad because let's not forget, many men and women died in the war and would not be coming home. But life goes on for Garston, for me and for ever. I wondered what the future held for me, it would soon be the 1950s and 1960s and even 1970s. Life was changing for all of us.

The Eternal Fisherman

Garston continued to grow after the war. It was the industrial engine of Liverpool and consequently one of the most polluted. The river, used as a sewer for years, was dead. All the fish had been poisoned, the Garston shoreline polluted. Oil kept washing up and worst of all, a ship breaker's yard had made the shore into a scrap yard.

It makes me cry, why oh why have I had to suffer this agony. Watching my river die, watch as the shoreline I love dies in front of my eyes. It took millions of years to become a beautiful river full of fish, clean sparkling water, and now in the space of 100 years it has been killed.

I am in purgatory, my dreams are becoming nightmares. Maybe, just maybe, one day, man will see sense and stop the madness and give the river back its life. Still I have a few friends, there are still one or two fishing boats that fish from Garston but they have to sail out into Liverpool Bay. There are also men and women who grow vegetables on the allotments – just how it's been for hundreds of years. Children still play on the shore, in the mud and on the iron ships; I love their laughter and toughness, real children of the mud.

Despite the problem of industry and pollution, Garston has grown economically, giving jobs to all, the community spirit is still strong and an energetic confidence is everywhere. The 50s, 60s and 70s have seen numerous changes. Televisions, fridges, fashion, music especially music, rock and roll and then The Beatles who made our river and city famous all over the world. Let's not forget the Ferry across the Mersey. I first saw the ferry 800 years ago when the monks sailed across on it. At least boats still sail the Mersey, coming into Garston Docks, unloading thousands of tons of cargo that need hundreds of miles of railways – Garston is a hive of industry. But change is afoot, new technology, containerisation, and no more bananas once the life blood of the docks. There is also talk of slum clearance, once proud streets being knocked down, communities displaced, but nothing ever stays the same and well I know that. Not all change is for the better – look at my river.

Still I cast my net, catch a dream, and let's look back at how change affects one our Garston Dockers, a proud workforce, hard working men, men of honour, men with families and houses.

Here he is – watch out.

The Garston Docker

I am proud to be a Garston Docker, just like my father before me; in fact it was my father who got me the job. There is a saying now that you need a letter from God to get a job on the docks. It wasn't always like that; in the

Garston Docks

old days it was a very hard job, that's if you got a day's work. My dad and his mates stood in pens like animals waiting to see if the Boss Man picked them out for the chance to work. Many men went home disappointed only to come back the next day. It was so unfair, that the docker's got organised into unions and fought for their right to a full-time job, good conditions, a decent wage packet, pensions and safe working conditions. It was not easy for the dockers; it took years of battling with the bosses, sometimes bitter, strikes caused much hardship for families of the striking men.

Now we have all these benefits, but trouble is ahead, the Port Authorities now say we are over-manned and want to bring in new technology, containerisation they call it. As well as this they want cuts in other areas, affecting our wages and conditions.

Garston was built on the docks; we have been the engine house of Garston's growth. From way back when we only had the Old North Dock then the Salt Docks were added and now we have the Stalbridge Dock that swallowed

up the Salt Docks, the salt workers cottages and the Rock Island the fishermen used to live on for hundreds of years.

We exported coal, minerals, fruit, fuel oil and general cargo but we imported a lot more, timber, minerals, iron, fruit, steel, molasses and china clay.

We were the biggest importer of bananas in Britain and I once worked on the banana boats, I loved it. No-one went short of bananas in our street, it was a welcome treat to the kids, and they loved banana butties.

Banana boat and dredger

When the banana boats left I went on to the coal boats but have worked on timber boats as well.

I am in the "Blue Union"; we broke away from the "White Union" who dominated Liverpool North Docks.

31

That was a fight we eventually won; again it was bitter, it even split some families up.

My dad was a founder member of the union and also of the Garston Stevedores and Dockers Social Club, known for years as the "Blue Union" in Window Lane.

I married a girl from "Hollywood" the posh end of Garston – they had bathrooms and gardens. I live in Campania Street and we got a grant from the council to modernise. Now we have an indoor toilet and bathroom and a bigger kitchen.

A lot of streets have been knocked down this side of Window Lane, most of King Street, Sinclair Street, Shand Street, Dingle Vale, Dale View, Hughes Street, Byrom Street, Shakespeare Street, Banks Road, the old C.E. St. Michaels School and lots of other houses. They called it the slum clearance but what I do know is that many people were sad to leave and go to Speke, Skem or Halewood.

We are lucky, we still have Window Lane – lots of shops, good pubs and the Blue Union Social and the Woodcutters Club, churches for all different traditions, good schools, Holy Trinity and Banks Road and a good community spirit.

I went to Holy Trinity and my wife went to Banks Road School, I don't know where our kids will go.

I love our river. I have a little fishing boat berthed on the shore alongside the Breaker's Yard. I go out sailing with my mates, its magic bobbing up and down on the river. It's been said that the river is haunted around here, I don't know about that. I do know the Garston Channel is kept clear of silt because of the docks and you need to avoid the Garston Rocks. I have heard in times past that Garston had a Lighthouse on the Old Dock. I wonder if that is true? As they say about Garstonians "The mud in our blood". I say yes to that and yes to our river.

I'm also saving up for a car, everybody around here are getting cars, especially the Ford men. It's unbelievable, only eighty years ago it was horse and cart, then the trams, overhead railway and buses, now men go to the moon and fly to Australia. Time is speeding up and I am getting left behind. I saw a computer in the office last week – that scared me. My wife got a Hoover - we didn't even have carpets when I was a lad. She also got a washing machine, when I think of my poor Mam washing by hand and using a dolly tub – she did have a mangle though; I should know as my hand got stuck in it once.

Garston Docks

Colour television now – we didn't have a telly when I was a lad but we did have the Saturday matinee at the Empire. We had no bath but we did have Garston Baths where you could get a bath or have a swim all for a tanner (2½p).

I'm not into politics, unlike my dad who was a socialist and a Labour man. Well now we have someone called Maggie Thatcher, a Tory. She said "I will break the power of the Unions". I doubt it; break the dockers, the miners and the steel men, no chance. "The workers united will never be defeated". I heard that last week on the telly.

I like to go out with the wife at the weekend. We go to the Blue or sometimes the Woodies, they have good turns on, a game of Bingo and best of all, a few pints.

Anyway let's hope things stay as good as this. I've got a good job, I'm buying my own little house and I'm in good health. Talking about health, I did break my leg playing football for the Blue. My wife said "No more football, it's not worth it". We will see – the lads took me to Garston Hospital, they couldn't help. Mind you we are lucky we have our own Garston Hospital, let's hope it stays.

There you go – see you again, I'm going for a pint – don't tell the wife.

The Eternal Fisherman

Hallelujah! I have good news, it seems human beings are realising the damage they are doing to the planet and the beautiful rivers they have poisoned.

Our River Mersey is now a lot cleaner; it is now no longer used as a sewer. The fish are returning, the river is coming back to life, it sparkles again. Hopefully no more oil will desecrate its water.

Maybe one day the children will swim in its splashing waves or play on a clean beach again. The ship-builders yard is no longer working but there are still wrecks on the shore – maybe one day it will be cleared.

It is now a New Millennium; I have inhabited these shores for a thousand years. I have seen so many changes, caught so many dreams and seen a few nightmares. Hopefully, they are over, maybe one day I will be allowed to rest and I will go home to the Great River beyond the clouds.

Tom the Docker was correct in his fears, the eighties and nineties saw tremendous changes in Garston. The lady Thatcher did take on the dockers, the miners and the steel men. She took on everyone and won. She said things had to change and change they did. Most of the Garston Dockers were made redundant, most of the mines in the country shut and most steel plants shut. Railways were privatised as nearly every other industry was. Garston and Speke were decimated over the years. The Bottle Works shut, the Gas Works shut, the Match Works closed, and the Tannery has now closed. Evans Medical, The Metal Box and Dunlop are all shut down and many others went the same way. It was called a slump, thousands put on the Dole, people left with no hope, the Great Depression it was called.

Communities were broken, little shops closed. Window Lane lost many small shops as did the village – again not their fault. Supermarkets took over, Retail Parks grew massive, and the car was King. Sunday was no longer a day of rest, we have 24 hour shopping, the lights never go out.

Still, Garston has a strong community spirit, we're all in it together come hell or high water.

New words are heard, SPEKE/GARSTON PARTNERSHIP, REGENERATION, PATHFINDERS, EUROPEAN MONEY, CONSULTATION, PARTICIPATION, EDUCATION, a whole new language. The language of regeneration, the men in suits came and told us what was needed to make Garston great again. There would be pain, no gain without pain. Take the medicine it is for your own good.

We now have a new Village Hall, millions of trees lining the roads, new industrial estates, new housing developments, new schools, new airport, a new sailing club, a coastal park and new jobs – a lot different from our industrial past but still, jobs for all that.

I have prattled on; we must cast our net for the last time. This man has many dreams; he likes to share them with the community. He has been through the changes we have talked about; he has grown from a boy to a man in the last sixty years. He is a true Garstonian, a true man of the mud, let's hear his story.

The Mud Man

I am a Mud Man and proud of it! Mud, glorious mud is in my blood. People ask me what is a Mud Man or Mud Woman. Well first of all it is not an insult – it's a bit like the term Cockney in London. They had to be born within the sound of Bow Bells. Well a Mud Man has to be born "under the bridge" in Garston and live between the Bridge and the Garston Shore with its Banks of Mud. Since history began with the Garston fishermen a thousand years ago until now with the docks and coastal park, Garstonians have worked and played alongside the River of Mud.

Garston shore

I was born in 1948 in Window Lane above the Fishmongers, there you go – fish again – mind you these fish were not caught in the Mersey, the only thing you could catch in the Mersey when I was a boy, was the "lurgey" – don't ask me what the "lurgey" is.

My Dad worked in the Bottle Works. My Mum didn't go out to work when I was a little boy but after I started school she went to work in the Mirror Works.

I loved growing up in Garston. Window Lane had hundreds of shops, fish shops, butchers, grocers, dairy, newsagents, dry cleaners, clothes shops, ironmongers, chippies, cake and wool shops, I used to go to the "Canterbury" for my Gran with a jug, to get a jug of brown ale with it's foaming bubbly head. I always had a sip!

At the top of the lane was the Gasworks, at the bottom the Bottle Works and in between all kinds of factories. When the buzzers and klaxons went for work, Window Lane thronged with crowds all rushing to work.

I loved to go out to play with my friends, we didn't play in Window Lane, as it was a bit busy. The 66 bus used to go up and down the lane and I remember it once ran over and killed a friend of mine. That frightened us!

We were lucky we had parks, one big one on Banks Road and three little parks in the streets. Besides the parks we had the streets, the Garston Shore, over the Iron Bridge and the play centre at Banks Road School. We always had something to do, we didn't watch much telly. In fact we didn't have a telly. In fact we didn't have a telly until I was eight in 1956.

Not much on telly then, the Wooden Tops – Bill and Ben – Rag Tag and Bobtail and Picture Book. Nowadays the telly is never off – very sad.

I went to Holy Trinity, my sisters went to Banks Road, don't ask me why but that's the way it was.

School was basic three R's, reading – writing – arithmetic; we did have a football team though.

Holy Trinity Church and School

I left school at 15 – couldn't wait to get a job, get some money – mind you my Mum took most of it for my keep.

My first job was at a Beer Bottler called Kings where me and my three mates became second men on dray wagons. In other words we delivered beer and drank a bit too – very naughty considering we had only just left school.

There were lots of jobs to be had in Garston in the 60s and 70s. I was sacked from the dray wagons, a job I loved, for going on strike. I always was a bit of a firebrand. I then got a job in the Mirror and Picture Works as an apprentice Guillotine Operator; the money was rubbish but I was learning a trade. The problem was, there was no-one to teach me. I was expected do the job after a few hours of tuition from the Boss, a Mr Jonathan. After I cut the heads off the Mona Lisa I got a warning from the Boss. I decided then to find a new job.

I was still only 17, I was courting and I wanted to leave home and get my own house. My Mum and Dad now lived in Stanley Street just off Window Lane. There were now six children – me the eldest, I wanted more room for myself.

I liked to go for a pint with my girlfriend. Garston was a friendly community and I enjoyed a good time. My Mum still goes to Church. Maybe I will go back one day, at the moment I need a new job. Mum said "I will pray for you to get a job".

Next day I got one in the Tannery in Window Lane. This is my third job within 500 yards of our house.

I started work in the Tannery on a cold snowy day, it was freezing but I liked it as there was a great team spirit, That is to say we are all in it together. We are hard men and it was hard work. I was a trimmer on the flesher.

The sixties brought great change. Lots of houses were knocked down on the dock side of the lane. Most of the people were sorry as they scattered to the wind. Everyone under 18 wanted to join a band and be as famous as The Beatles, Merseybeats, Rory Storm or the Searchers. Liverpool was the place to be, the centre of town had the Cavern, and we in Garston had the Winter Gardens.

I was too busy saving to buy a house. I would be the first in our family to own a home of my own. No more paying rent or paying my keep. I hadn't a clue what a mortgage was but I got one, so me and my wife had our own house. Oh yes! I forgot to tell you I got married – went up the steps at St Michael's – this pleased Mum but not Dad – don't ask why. Then we moved into Hardy Street, a nice street. I worked hard, so did my wife at the Match Works. We even got a grant to do up the house, indoor toilet, bathroom, new windows, new kitchen, it was great. So hundreds of houses on our side of the lane got extensions and double glazing. As well as this, new houses went up in place of the knocked down houses in King Street, Banks Road and Window Lane.

Match Works

I heard there were jobs to be had in the Ford Motor Co., better money than the Tan Yard and they said less smelly and better conditions, pensions and sick pay. It was now 1975, we had a baby, the wife finished work and I finished at the tan-yards to go to Fords. I hated the job, I was only there for six weeks, I didn't like shifts and neither did the wife so I left.

Still there were plenty of jobs to be had, Garston was still flourishing but signs of what was to come had started. Supermarkets were opening – little shops closing and the little factories were struggling.

Yet we were lucky, I got a job in Evans Medical because I was good at football. I agreed to play for their football team. Life was good, we got a colour telly, fitted wardrobes, posh washing machine and fitted carpets, and we had never had it so good.

Despite this there was a lot of national unrest, the Unions were fighting and politicians were not happy. Locally wasn't too bad but there was industrial unrest, especially amongst the miners and dockers.

We had Wilson for Labour and Heath for Conservative. We had the 3 day week because of power cuts caused by the miners' strike. Then Heath brought in wages linked to inflation. We kept getting rises and thought we were better off – we weren't!

Then along came James Callaghan. The 70s ended with the Winter of Discontent. Liverpudlians and some Garstonians were at the forefront of industrial action. The media made much of this - rubbish on the streets and dead bodies not getting buried. That was it, the next thing Margaret Thatcher was elected and the unions were toast. She swept away unions, not without a fight though. She said we must modernise and downsize and close if we were not efficient. Well unemployment went through the roof and Speke and Garston got a hammering.

In the meantime I had a lot of different hair do's, long hair, skin head and even a perm – I never got over that! The children – we had two, now liked school and holidays abroad, we even got a video recorder.

Then, you know what hit the fan, mass unemployment, millions on the dole, factories shutting or shedding jobs. Dunlop went, the first of many, now Evans Medical became Glaxo, more redundancies, Metal Box shed jobs, Standard Triumph closed down, Brough Drums closed as did the Mirror and Picture Works, Gas Works, Bottle Works and the Docks lost jobs, and it was endless.

Garston went into mourning, the slow death of the streets and factories and pubs. Under the bridge was becoming a ghost town and within years the Garston I grew up in had changed beyond recognition.

I took heart up in the shore though. I walked with the children; the River always makes worries smaller putting our little preoccupations into perspective.

Liverpool had riots in 1981 in Toxteth. A shock in the short term – the answer – a garden festival. I was glad of that because in 1984 I was another victim of redundancy and millions were on the dole but I managed to get a job at the garden festival and enjoyed this but the pay was rubbish.

Rubbish is an apt word as the garden festival was built on a huge rubbish dump. The problem was the garden festival was only seasonal work so it was difficult.

The Militant Tendency was in power in Liverpool and caused much argument for and against, eventually they lost power and this cost more jobs.

From being the industrial heart of Liverpool, Garston became a bit of a sick man. In fact now we were part of the European Union we were designated a Special Objective One Aid Area as we were so poor. The area looked neglected, houses and shops were boarded up, factories closed, unemployment high and young people seemed to have no hope. There was still hope though; we still had our schools and churches, and a bit of the old community spirit.

I was lucky; I got a job with the City Council grave-digging. I've heard all the jokes, it's not what you know, it's who you know!

Some cynics say we should bury Garston. I said it's not dead yet - give it time. What was dead though was a "job for life" with pension and sick pay.

Thatcherism and Monetarism would bring us success, well it did for the rich.

We all had to tighten our belts. I liked my job, the kids were happy at school, the wife had a part time job and we liked our street.

I'm not really into politics, my favourite saying is "they're all the same" and I still believe that. Yet I went along with all my mates when we had an election, I voted for Labour. Thatcher battered us and John Major bored us. So we sent for the new kid on the block, smiling Tony Blair. He didn't seem like Labour to me, he was too posh, nevertheless he was New Labour, it sounded like a new soap powder - New Daz, it washes whiter. So in 1997 we had New Labour, let's see if it helped us in Garston.

The first thing I noticed was the men in suits, and then giant billboards went up, the new words – jargon I call it.

REGENERATION – that was the miracle word.

That's what we had to listen to for years on end. Men in suits – beware!

One thing they like doing is demolition, not for them preserving history or community pride in their old buildings, no it was "away" with the old and in with the "new". So more streets went the way of the bulldozer, when Stanley Street was demolished my Mum and Dad had to go to live in sheltered accommodation.

Bankfield House

Banks Road had a beautiful Edwardian school – it had to go –they have a new school now (a prefab).

The Village Hall – our only green playing field went under the concrete. Eventually the old Community Centre, much loved in the community "Bankfield House" was demolished – madness. The old Holy Trinity Church has gone – sad. The old swimming baths gone for a new leisure centre on another green field.

Maybe I'm just an old fossil living in the past.

The men in suits might be right! Things have to change to keep up in the modern world. Will the community survive? Well all the houses called the Ship Streets have gone – demolished. Not fit for purpose, some of them in Banks Road were built to replace the 60s slum clearances, now they are going as well.

Still the new houses look smart so maybe the men in suits are right, or is it all about profit for the developers – you make up your mind.

Never mind, life goes on as it has done for a thousand years in Garston that has seen many changes in that time.

Like the river it just keeps rolling along.

The Ancient Church of St Michaels's still looks down on the people and river, watches our coming and going from the Monks to the Mud Men, it has seen so much over such a long time.

One thing for sure, Garstonians will just get on with it.

I should have a job for life – or death if you know what I mean.

My children have got jobs on the Mersey Estuary Park. I hope one day they can afford a house – please.

My wife has finished work and is thankful for her nice house in Hardy Street; it's definitely not getting knocked down.

Anyway, I'm going for a walk up the shore. I love our River; we have a new Coastal Park now. I love to dream along the shore of the past and future. You know the other day I felt sure someone was walking with me, I looked around and all I saw was the River, it seemed to whisper in my ear everything will be alright. When I looked up in the sky a cloud looking like a fishing boat floated off to heaven.

Sorry - I'm dreaming.

Come on take my hand, we look to the future with hope.

Garston Stones

The Eternal Fisherman

The Mud Man is right, I am floating off to the great river beyond the sky. I have lived my dream; erased my nightmare. I am free again. I leave you with this poem.

Catching Dreams

My boat lay beached, her back broken
All voyages ended, all commands spoken
Strong nets caught river fish by the ton
Wet salmon reflect rainbows in the sun

The sleepy town's dreams came drifting by
I catch them in nets and sing a lullaby
To the children dancing on the sea shore
Telling them tales of ancient folklore

Of the times we fished on the ebbing tide
Catching moonbeams on the water wide
The splashing waves have a power to renew
Bathing us in silver stars and morning dew.

The Eternal Fisherman - 2

I thought I had finished with this tale, especially when the Man who called himself the Mud Man told his story! but it seems I am not, now his wife whom he calls his Garston Rose, wants to tell us of her experiences; and why not?

The Mud Man was right my spirit did leave the River for a while and float off to the Great harbour in the sky, at last I had found my way home. But as the Eternal Fisherman I am always available, and it seems my spirit is needed now.

I know I am needed now the spirit of the Mud Man is low, he has suffered many setbacks in the last few years. Let's listen to his wife's story, as she tells us of the many changes that have taken place on the River and in the Village of Garston since I have been away. This has affected many lives, some say for the better others think not. One who thinks not is The Mud Man who feels the history and spirit of the community, on the shore and in the village, are being destroyed by shortsighted planners and developers.

Let's now catch up on our story.

The Garston Rose

Garston Rose Queen

Yes! That's what my husband – the man you know as the Mud Man calls me – My Garston Rose. It's just as well I like it, my husband has called me by pet name since we were married 40 years ago. We still live in the first house we bought in Hardy Street, although we are thinking of selling up and moving into a smaller place – maybe one of those retirement flats they're building.

The house is getting too much to look after now, especially since my man got ill.

My two daughters have also moved out, so we don't need all the space; we are so pleased they have got places of their own. We have come a long way over these last 40 years, when I think of it we have been through a lot just like everyone else around us in Garston. Just lately though it has got my man down, so much he loved has gone, a lot of his friends have gone too. I thought he would bounce back but his bounce seems to have gone, someone has let the air out. I keep telling him to be grateful for what we've got. A nice house, good friends, a supportive family and especially our girls and beautiful grandchildren. That's why I keep telling John to count our blessings, he say's he does, and I believe him. When he's playing with the lads, taking them the park, or football, or his favourite, walking up the shore with them, he always comes back with a smile on his face. He wants the boys to love the river and shore like he himself to become real mudboys. John always tells me, he comes alive up the shore, alongside the river. He loves to watch the, sparkling waves, the changeable cloud formations, the reeds singing in the slightest breeze, the call of the curlew and seagulls, and looking at the Welsh mountains in the distance. He loves to pray and contemplate the world around him, and often he said "I feel a Spirit around me" he tells me this often explaining, "I feel I am a part of the sun, the river, the earth, the sky." All I know is he comes home in a much better state of mind when he returns home, sometimes hours later. The lads liked going to the shore with their granddad, this pleased John so much, he had found his soul mates. They loved to fly kites on the sea breeze, to skim stones on the river's waves, and to paddle in the soft mud. I always had to wash the muddy clothes when they came home covered in mud. I asked John, "Is there any chance you can bring them home clean John?"

He laughed and said "A bit of mud has never hurt anyone, especially mudboys."

He wanted them to grow up loving the shore, the river, and God's creation...

He often repeated these words, still if it keeps him happy I didn't mind, but clouds were on the horizon.

One night he began to rant on about the damage being done to his home in Garston, they are destroying our history, our heritage, our buildings.

Apparently, the powers that be were demolishing The Garston Hotel, a jewel in the crown of the village, and

John was angry about it and broken hearted. I wasn't surprised they were knocking down the hotel as it had lay as a burnt out shell for years. "That's the point" he said, and went on to tell me a story of arson and mystery, that has led to this sorry end for the Garston Hotel.

Garston Hotel

I must admit though the Garston Hotel was once a very impressive building with a great history, a grand old dame of the town.

When The Garston Hotel was first built in the 19th century it was a sign that Garston had arrived. At the time Garston was still independent from Liverpool and determined to show they were no backwater. This small town already had its own docks and railways, a shopping area and now it had its own first class hotel, this would be used by visiting captains of industry. John often told me the story of sea captains who used the hotel to stop in, not only that, they used the hotels as a lookout. The Garston Hotel was built with a lantern on the top, from here the captains and owners of ships could watch their vessels sailing up the river into port. When the captains spotted their ships they would send a messenger to the docks to alert the harbourmaster. The ships had to sail carefully into the Garston channel and avoid at all costs the notorious Garston Rocks which were clearly visible when the tide was out, but lay black and deadly when the tide was high, laying in wait for any straying ships.

Those days are well gone, and so is the Garston Hotel. I remember when first going out with John one of the places we went to was the Garston Hotel, it was thought then that it had a bit of class - it even had a commissioner in uniform on the very opulent entrance, he used to salute as we entered. Now it has gone! And in its place a block of characterless flats.

I tell John not to get upset, but he does, and then he rants on about gangsters, corruption, and greedy money men. "It's all about money these days – money – money – money" then he just stares into space, looking dreamy – most likely he is dreaming he is on top of the Garston Hotel looking up the river Mersey waiting for his ship to come in.

It got even worse for John when he finished work, he had decided to retire, from his work at Allerton cemetery. To be honest though I was happy when he retired, the work was getting a bit strenuous for him, digging graves and landscaping work was a young man's job. I looked forward to having more time with John. He had a nice pension so things looked good for the future. It didn't quite work out that way though. I didn't realise John would miss his work so much, so I was pleased when he said he was going to take up voluntary work in the community. He worked in the community centre and joined many community groups. He loved Garston and its people, so I was sure this would help with his mood of helplessness. I was wrong! Community work is a thankless task – no pay – lots of headaches, and most of the headaches were around money. Most community organisations need public funding to survive and this money was hard to come by, a continuous battle.

I loved music and dance, I would put my records on and try to get John dancing.

"Come on Mud Man! Cheer up, let's have a dance?" Dancing is how we met all those years ago in the Winter Gardens a lively place up the village. Those days we had no booze, only coke – the drink, not the stuff they put up their nose these days.

Great bands have played at the Wint's – Rory Storm and the Hurricanes – The Beatles – The Mersey Beats – and we danced the night away to them all.

We laughed a lot, and hoped to meet the love of our life, or at least get walked home. One night I put my music on, then! John went into a rant "You wouldn't believe what they are doing now?"

I feared the worse, "What?" "They are demolishing the Winter Gardens now, criminal it is." He went on for half an hour before he finished. I felt sorry for John, another place he loved had gone, but it wasn't exactly the Blackpool Ballroom, and had ceased to be a dancehall years ago, its last use was as a furniture warehouse. Still I was a little sorry myself it was going, mostly for nostalgic reasons than anything else – memories that is all we would have soon.

As far as John was concerned though it was another nail in the coffin of Garston and its history.

Surely there were positive things happening as well in Garston? They were building new houses on Banks Road and where the ship streets once stood. The houses were nice they had a bit of character as well as gardens. The city of Liverpool had been awarded the status of The European City of Culture for 2008, and close on its tail Garston through the endeavours of local artists launched a scheme to be The Village of Culture. What's the use of all this John would say if they destroy our heritage in the process. "I am going for a walk" he would say, this was his mantra, and up the shore he would go coming home hours later. What he found up there I don't know, but he always came home more peaceful after his wanderings.

He often met friends up there and they sat and talked solving the problems of the world – or at least Garston. Even if he didn't meet anyone up there, he said he was not alone, not with the river as a whispering friend. I said to him "Be careful who you tell these things to, they will send for the green van." He then told me I didn't understand these things and if you listen you will hear the spirit of the river.

I don't know about the river; but I do know the spirit of the people of Liverpool was certainly lifted by the award of The City of Culture to our great city.

We both enjoyed the wonderful year that was the city of culture, it was a shot in the arm for Liverpool it also put us on the map again. John and I attended many events through the year, from the major ones like the opening Nativity play, to big events at St George's Hall, to the incredible giant spider in the rain, and we even went Lambanana mad and searched and found all of them around the city. We went to big art exhibitions in the Walker and the Tate Galleries, and smaller ones around the City. We also went to our theatres, large and small, and finally we went to river spectaculars when they were on.

John was pleased when he told me the first Lambanana was made in Garston at a studio in the old Matchworks site.

The Garston we love had its own culture year – The Village of Culture - we were pleased the Headquarters of this project was to be the old Toxteth Technical School – Known as Tocky Tech – it was hoped that this plan would save the building from demolition because it had been empty for some years. The sun shone brightly for the launch of the Village of Culture. The underlying theme of the summer would be that Garston would declare independence from Liverpool and show off its own culture and difference. Garston only became part of Liverpool in

51

1902 and even now people still regard us as separate from the city. The Tocky Tech school was to be The Embassy for independant Garston, which meant we would have our own passports, our own money, our own army, and our own president. The day of the friendly revolution, the bands played, the people marched, the president rolled in atop his vintage car surrounded by his presidential guard. There were awards made, gongs given out, and titles given to the great and good, and even real politicians shaking hands and kissing babies, this for me didn't bode well for the new republic of Garston. There was a nod to Garston's past with a privateer called Dawson who once sailed out of Liverpool, ransacked a French ship called *Carnatic*, making Dawson so rich he was able to buy Garston, and gain himself the mayorship of Liverpool, and then retire to the now named Carnatic Hall. The trade of privateering was legal. All you had to get was a letter of Marque authorising you to take any ship of any country at war with Britain. The Launch of the Republic was a great success, the president was sworn in, the drink flowed, chocolates were given out, everyone had a good time – then nothing.

Garston Embassy

That's about all I remember about the Village of Culture, it all ended like a damp squib, the embassy has reverted to an empty school and an unsure future. This gave John another chance to rant. He felt the good people of Garston had been used by the powers that be to make some money and when they have, they move on to another community to make another pot of money.

Something that cheered us both up was the changes made at the Pierhead. Like most Liverpudlians we have sweet memories of the Pierhead, so we were worried when yet another improvement scheme was proposed for the waterfront with its three graces, ferries, and pulsating river. We need not have worried the changes have only added to the appearance of the iconic waterfront. The new people's museum a contempary style, very different from the classical style of the Three Graces, yet the angular shapes of the museum contrast well with the old. Setting the whole scene off was a wonderful canal, joining the old Leeds – Liverpool Canal with the Pierhead, a magnificent feat of engineering all beautifully enclosed in granite blocks, giving it a solid permament feel. We often sail on the ferries enjoying the views and memories of New Brighton and days on the beach. We wished the ferry could sail down the river to Garston and drop us off at home.

Then another setback for John, the powers that be announced the demolition of Garston's most iconic building. The Sir Alfred Jones Hospital had been built for the people of Garston in 1912. Standing atop a hill called Kettle Nook it had looked benignly down on the village for nearly a hundred years, now it was to be knocked down. Sir Alfred Lewis Jones had bequeathed £10,000 towards the cost of a new hospital. The hospital was built in the Queen Anne style and was very attractive, and named after the main benefactor Sir Alfred Lewis Jones. Two weeks before the announcement of the plans to demolish the hospital we were at the Pierhead admiring a newly restored statue of Sir Alfred Lewis Jones, a sad

Garston Hospital

coincidence. It is a magnificent statue incredibly detailed remembering Sir Alfred's achievements in commerce he managed a shipping line. In medicine he was the first chairman of the School of Tropical Medicine. In Garston he is also remembered for bringing bananas into the port of Garston, he also – so legend says – went around the village with a hand cart with bananas on, trying to get people to try this new fancy fruit.

John, as I said, was active in the community and formed an action group to oppose the demolition of the hospital, they fought hard getting a thousand signatures on a petition. The action group demonstrated at the Town Hall, John even spoke at the council planning meeting, but none of these efforts made much difference and the demolition went ahead. It was not that the action group opposed progress they just felt the old hospital was important to the heritage and history of Garston, they also felt it had architectural merit, although they failed in their attempt to get it listed.

Many people were devastated when the demolition went ahead, especially John, who went into a sort of depression, becoming very cynical about town planners, politicians, bankers, and building companies.

I know John will get over this setback, he has in the past, over the years we have overcome a lot together. We have too much going for us, we have many friends and good neighbours, a close loving family, beautiful children and grandchildren. Less importantly, but very important to John, he still had his beloved shore and River and he always says just let the River wash over you its healing waters will work its magic.

The Eternal Fisherman - Farewell

Well the journey goes on, I thought my time on the river was over but I was wrong! The man you know as the Mud Man needs my help. I will help him get over his recent setbacks, he will hear the river whisper to him and heal and console him. I am the eternal fisherman and anyone who listens to my message will find happiness in the beauty of the river as it flows in the veins of those who love it. I once fished this river, then I watched it die, the river was poisoned by man's ignorance, then all the fish died, and what was a magnificent river became a sewer. Now a miracle has happened, the river lives again and fish swim once again in its clean water. What was dead is now reborn, and that can be true for men as it can for rivers. Our friend the Mud Man has the spirit but at the moment he is a bit despondent but he will recover his joy.

He was too modest to tell you but he supported for years the Mersey Basin campaign which worked hard to clean the river up and they succeeded. He also supported the community efforts to make the old airport a part of a Garston coastal park alongside the river and in this they succeeded and gave Garston people a fantastic place to relax and enjoy the flora and fauna. It is maturing now and the meadows and shoreline are bursting with new life. There is also a brand new Liverpool sailing club on the coastal park overlooking the now clean river. The old club was burned down so it was a great day for local sailors when the new club - designed to look like a sailing ship – was officially opened by H.R.H. Princess Anne.

Liverpool Sailing Club

The clay boulder cliffs alongside the river are still eroding and have lost hundreds of yards over the time scale of this story 800 years from monks to Mud Men. In that time we have watched the seasons come and go, the village change into a town, then become part of the great city of Liverpool; see a decline, then regeneration now an uncertain future. One thing will stay constant – the river, the bluebells will bloom every spring on the boulder clay cliffs, and my spirit will still be there in the river, in the sky, in the clouds, and in the earth, all you have to do is seek it. Let's finish with a wise tale from the Mud Man to his grandchildren, it gives us all hope for the future.

Grandad's Story

We had a beautiful river, full of fish. All the people loved the river – they had picnics on its banks – the children swam in its crystal clear water – and the fishermen caught fish.

Sammy Salmon was a fisherman he had a little boat, all was well for many years.

One day big machines came and built an oil terminal. Mr Greedy Guts wanted to make lots of money, his oil tankers came up and down the river to discharge oil.

Sammy Salmon went to see Mr Greedy and told him to be careful with his tankers as the river was clean and any oil spill would ruin the fishing. With that Sammy gave Greedy a fish to eat. Greedy Guts enjoyed the fish and promised to keep the river clean.

One day a tanker crashed into a sandbank, oil gushed out turning the river black, and all the oil poisoned the fish.

Sammy Salmon was heartbroken, he picked up lots of dead fish, he decided to take one to Greedy Guts to eat, but Greedy Guts could not eat it as it was poisoned.

Mr Greedy Guts realised his folly and promised to clean up the river, this he did, and closed down the oil terminal. Mr Greedy then built two fishing boats, one he gave to Sammy Salmon and the other to himself. Greedy Guts then became the river's friend, from then on he was known as the Fishermen's Friend.

MORAL TO THE STORY - YOU CAN'T EAT OIL